The Flowering Cactus

The Flowering

Cactus

An informative Guide,
Illustrated in
Full-Color Photography,
to One of the Miracles of
America's Southwest.

EDITED BY RAYMOND CARLSON

PHOTOGRAPHS AND TECHNICAL DATA
BY R. C. AND CLAIRE MEYER PROCTOR

SKETCHES AND DESIGN BY GEORGE M. AVEY

McGraw-Hill Book Co., Inc.
NEW YORK · TORONTO · LONDON

To those who have found

enchantment and peace

in the land of

the flowering cactus —

This volume is dedicated.

ACKNOWLEDGMENTS

Gratitude is extended to Robert H. Peebles, senior agronomist of the United States Field Station, Department of Agriculture, Sacaton, Arizona, for his advice in preparing the text of this book and in selecting correct botanical names for the species illustrated. Although Mr. Peebles' main work is research in cotton improvement, he is recognized as an authority on Arizona plants, including cacti.

Lithogravure by H. S. Crocker Co., Inc.,
San Francisco, Calif.

Typography by Morneau Typographers,
Phoenix, Arizona

Contents

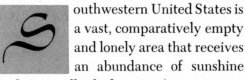

Land of
THE FLOWERING CACTUS

Southwestern United States is a vast, comparatively empty and lonely area that receives an abundance of sunshine and tragically little rain (see map on page 94). Here the sun is an arrogant dictator, an implacable tyrant of heat and light to whom all living things must bow in order to survive. Here in this arid land, through generations of adaptation, man, animal, and plant have not only survived but flourished. There is no terror in the rigors of the sun when you are properly equipped, when Nature has given you strange but effective tools and garments to deflect the strong rays of that source of light and heat that governs all life.

This is no ordinary land; nor is anything in it ordinary.

This is a land of miracles, of superlatives, of strange and wondrous things. The greatest miracle of all — a miracle of beauty and exquisite coloring, of fragile loveliness and design unsurpassed in the plant kingdom — is the blossom of the flowering cactus. Members of the cactus family so dominate the landscape and are such an intimate part of it that this can truly be called "the land of the flowering cactus."

Mapmakers of early days, dismayed by the vastness and strangeness they came to explore, labeled it "the great American desert" and went on with their measuring sticks to more familiar and less harsh terrain. It begins to the east where the great fertile plains break off into the sage and rocky washes of New Mexico and western Texas, and ends to the west where the rising slopes of the high coastal range form the spinal column of California. Beyond this range lies the cool, blue Pacific, whose moisture is sparsely bestowed on the thirsty wilderness eastward because the snow-clad peaks of that coastal range form a barrier to storms that should normally sweep in westward from the sea.

This arid expanse includes western Texas, southern California, Arizona, New Mexico, Nevada, southern and eastern Utah, southern and western Colorado, with the exceptions of portions of these states where mountains, like green oases, shoulder forests against the sky, and where, in a few places, waters from rivers dammed have been turned into irrigation ditches to make the dry acres bloom. No respecter of man-made boundaries between nations, the flowering cactus claims also as part of its domain all of Baja California, most of the state of Sonora, Mexico, and much of the remainder of Mexico.

Above the border this is America's desert. To the uninitiated the word connotes sandy wastes devoid of life in any form. This desert of which we speak is actually filled with life, and its soil, for the most part, could grow fence posts if given enough water. Limited by an annual rainfall of from 4 to 11 inches (there are years when there is no rain at all), curious plant forms have developed admirable ways to exist, even flourish, with

BEAVER-TAIL CAC
Opuntia bas

6

COB CACTUS — *Lobivia Hertrichiana*

CANDELABRUM CACTUS – *Opuntia imbricata*

9

little moisture. This desert is turbulent yet tranquil; forbidding but wonderfully attractive with a charm and a beauty all its own.

Those from greener and more placid landscapes are at first repelled by the monotony of this land, of the gray-green foliage, the glare of sunlight, the empty skies, the extravagant colors of cliff and canyon, the measureless mesas and plateaus, the ever bristling threat of the sharp and thorny points of plants, the brutal marks left in the earth by the sculpturing tools of time and weather. Days and seasons flow into each other without change, so that the passing of time becomes a rhythmic monotony, and that, too, is unattractive to those who are accustomed to their years being divided into four orderly, understandable acts. The land is so vast and so durably constructed that it defies the more obvious changes of spring, summer, autumn, and winter.

The very insignificance of man in such an immensity is appalling. When the balladeers, singing of this arid country, refer to it as the "wide open spaces," they have not sacrificed accuracy for the sake of musical idiom. Where the average density of population in the United States is 49.9 persons per square mile, county after county in this desert land can count less than 2 persons per square mile, and one county, Mohave in Arizona, has a sparse population of 0.6 persons per square mile. "Land of time enough and room enough" is not, by any means, poetic fancy.

Yet civilizations flourished here long before the Pilgrims came to Plymouth Rock. Throughout the Southwest are thousands of prehistoric ruins, monuments to antiquity whose empty rooms

whisper of little brown people who once found the land generous, but finally perished or were forced to leave when the rains ceased to come. A long time ago, so long ago that even the most learned of scholars do not know when, certain Indians came and settled down, and their descendants are here today. They are the Paiutes, Navajos, Hopis, Supais, Apaches, Yavapais, Pimas, Papagos, Maricopas, Mohaves, Chemehuevis, and some of the Pueblo tribes of New Mexico. For generations they have shared this land with the flowering cactus.

When the Spaniards came, almost a century before the *Mayflower* landed at Plymouth, they found the Papagos and Pimas, children of the desert, peaceful and primitive, drawing an existence from the bare, arid land. But sweeping out from desert hills came a less peaceful tribe, the Apaches, who made the land untenable for Spaniard and, for some three centuries, anyone else who attempted to move into their domain. Now the Apaches are affluent cattlemen, drive station wagons, and are friendly with their neighbors. They, like the desert, have become less hostile with the passing of the years.

Early American pioneers, in the beginning of the great western migration, avoided the desert country because it had nothing to offer the homeseeker and settler. Water holes were few and far between. Travel was not only arduous but dangerous. One road, for instance, *El Camino del Diablo* (Devil's Highway), which skirted what is now the Arizona-Sonora border, claimed the lives of six travelers as late as this decade, and there are graves all along its path, evidence that the ways of the desert can be hard.

The first important migration into the

OCOTILLO
Fouquieria splendens

11

Southwest was that of the Mormon pioneers in the middle of the last century. The Mormons settled first in the Valley of the Great Salt Lake in Utah and sent their people to establish colonies all through the Southwest. One of the reasons they chose their homesites as they did was the belief, expressed by some of their leaders, that the land was so ungracious that no one else would want it. They could live in peace and worship as they wished without molestation from their neighbors. They called this kingdom that they were to set up in the wastelands of earth "Deseret."

The flowering cactus was beginning to have company other than Indians.

With the coming of the automobile age and the highway engineer, people no longer shunned the arid land. Modern highways were built to cross it in every direction, making it of easy access, lessening the dangers of travel. Now only the more intrepid traveler seeking out the unfrequented places travels with shovel and extra can of water.

Motorists soon found that the Southwest offered untold delight in scenic wonders. In California there was Death Valley and the Joshua Forest, now a national monument. In Arizona were such travel shrines as Grand Canyon, Monument Valley, Painted Desert and Petrified Forest, the Sonoran desert, (two portions of which have been set aside to forever protect and enshrine two members of the cactus family, the saguaro and the organ-pipe), prehistoric ruins (permanent monuments to the impermanency of man), and landmarks to the memory of Spanish Conquest (the missions of Tumacacori and San Xavier). In New Mexico were located White Sands, Shiprock, and other scenic and prehis-

toric places. A fantastic panorama of canyon and eroded wilderness of stone and color made southern and eastern Utah appear like illustrated pages from a prehistoric fairy tale (Bryce and Zion National Parks, Bridges and Arches National Monuments), and the scarred but richly painted land of cliffs and buttes and spires marked the paths carved by the San Juan, Green, and Colorado rivers in their journey to the sea. In southwestern Colorado were the prehistoric city Mesa Verde, and other places of antiquity and scenic interest.

Shortly after the beginning of this century there came to the desert, in increasing numbers, the health seekers. Where medicine had failed, the eternal sunshine and the light, dry air of the arid land succeeded. Uncounted thousands through the years have regained their health and found happiness in this, the once avoided land. They continue to come to this day, seeking ease, rest, and health, and more often than not their journey has been successful. There is largess in the land of the flowering cactus, and the blessings bestowed on the suffering have been many.

In recent years there has been a new and phenomenal development in travel to the Southwest. This is the ever-increasing number of strangers who come during winter and spring to avoid the harshness of weather in less favored parts of America. They come to rest in the sun, to escape the nervous tensions created by the pressure of everyday living in more populated areas of our land. They are repaid by serenity of mind and body.

These seekers after blessed moments of rest and tranquillity are coming in such numbers that in one desert city alone, a city with a normal population of 100,000, over 50,000 visitors come to swell the population every winter and spring. To tend to the needs and comforts of these seasonal visitors to the Southwest, a gigantic industry has been developed. The desert has finally gained an important place in the economic life of the land. It is almost poetic justice that an area that was once universally shunned is now being sought after by many. The flowering cactus, in a way, has become the symbol of a large and happy business.

These visitors are the ones who come to know the desert best, for they have the time, interest, patience, and curiosity to learn its secrets and are handsomely repaid for their efforts. They appreciate the dry, clean air which gives clarity to vista and zest to the morning. They delight in desert nights when stars appear, as if more brightly polished than stars elsewhere, and when the moon takes on a new luster, glowing so brightly at times that one can read a newspaper by its light without eyestrain. For them a desert trail has an infinity of wonders. Plant life, at first so odd, almost ominous, hospitably discloses its personality on better acquaintance, with each plant becoming familiar, readily giving up all of its intimate secrets to anyone with understanding and inquiring ways. Every plant has a story to tell. This wonder world of desert botany is packed with strange and curious things; so much so that its study is the greatest pleasure the desert has to offer.

The first thing that a study of desert plant life has to reveal is that all plants which bristle with spines, thorns, and needles are not necessarily members of the cactus family. A few plants in this category should be mentioned because they are so conspicuously a part of the desert scene and share with the flowering cactus the allure and attraction that desert lands have for so many people.

One of the handsome and graceful plants of the desert is the ocotillo *(Fouquieria splendens)*, sometimes called "slimwood" or "coachwhip." This large, thorny shrub sends forth slender, whip-like stems from a central base on the ground (see illustration on page 96). At times these plants will have as many as twenty stems from 10 to 15 feet in length. The stems normally are gray-green, so hard that Indians and early settlers used them for fences. Even today ocotillo (oh-co-*tee*-yo) fences are common in the Southwest. Quite often these transplanted stems will take root and grow, so that living fences are not unusual in an area where the unusual is an accepted fact.

When there is rainfall in spring and autumn, the ocotillo sends forth from its stems a covering of small leaves. The leaves function as all leaves do—for the manufacture of food. When the ground dries, the leaves drop off, which is one of the wise ways this plant has developed to conserve moisture. When spring comes, the ocotillo responds by putting on a cluster of waxy scarlet blossoms, 4 to 5 inches in length, at the very end of each stem. When these blossoms nod to the touch of light spring breezes, one has in the ocotillo a living bouquet.

The yucca *(yuck-uh)* family (see illustration on page 96) is a very showy desert clan, related not to the cactus but to the lily. The most imposing member of this family is the Joshua tree *(Yucca brevifolia)*, which grows up to 35 feet in height, and is so weirdly shaped as to

13

remind one of distant times and ages when dinosaurs and other creatures ruled all creation. A portion of the Mohave Desert of California, where these strange plants are found in abundance, has been set aside as Joshua Tree National Monument. A large Joshua forest is also found near Lake Mead, north of Kingman, in northwestern Arizona. Another interesting member of the yucca family is called "Spanish dagger" or "Spanish bayonet," (*Yucca baccata*) an apt name because of the dangerously sharp, spine-tipped branches; a feature of the plant (see illustration on page 96).

The agave (ah-*gah*-ve) is common in the higher elevations of the Southwest. One member of this family, the century plant (*Agave Parryi*), puts forth when it blooms a long towering stalk, the top of which is covered with yellow blossoms. A thicket of these plants blooming at the same time is a *memorable* sight (see illustration on page 96).

Even the trees in the desert have adapted themselves to a life of little rain and much sunshine. The palo verde (pal-oh-*vair*-day), a name from the Spanish meaning "green stick," has a green trunk, green limbs, green branches, green leaves and thorns. It sheds its small leaves in dry seasons, and puts them on when it rains. A bushy, spreading tree, it is not attractive until spring comes, when it is a cloud of shimmering yellow.

Cercidium microphyllum, the little-leaf palo verde, and *Cercidium floridum*, sometimes called the "blue palo verde" because of the slight bluish cast to its greenness, are two species found in the Southwest.

The tree most commonly associated with the desert regions is the mesquite (meh-*skeet*), the more prevalent species of which is *Prosopis juliflora*. Untold thousands of miles of barbed wire have been hung on fence poles made from this tree, and more untold thousands of campfires have been made from its wood, the most fragrant of all woods for burning. The tree bristles with sharp spines, and produces, after its flowering season, long, sweet bean pods.

The ironwood, *Olneya tesota*, a large thorny desert tree, attains a height of 30 feet with a trunk diameter of a foot and a half. The wood is very hard and heavy, a characteristic from which it derives its common name.

There is nothing quite like the wonders of the desert in spring. If there have been heavy rains in late winter, the desert floor is turned into a colorful carpet when millions of seeds, dormant perhaps for years, awaken to the magic touch of the season. Old-timers say you can expect an extravagant flower show in the arid land about every seven years, such is the instability of the rainfall.

But rain or no rain, the flowering cactus is always dependable, wearing the brightest of boutonnieres each and every year as a tribute to this gayest of seasons, and its quest is always an adventure.

The strange shapes found among members of the cactus family, with their showy blossoms, are unique in the plant kingdom. A cactus (from the Greek word *kaktos*, meaning a kind of spiny or prickly plant) bears little resemblance to other plants found in the world today. Their unknown ancestors, after centuries of existence in a region growing progressively drier, reduced their branches and twigs to spines, diminished their leaves to all but invisible scales or discarded them altogether for spines, with the skin of the plant producing the chlorophyll and transferring the function of food manufacture from the leaf to the trunk or stems of the plant. Continued reduction of stems and development of tissue for storing water often resulted in very spiny columns, globes, and thick pads or joints. Cacti have developed a complex organ, spirally arranged over the stems, known as the areole, a characteristic organ of the cactus plant and not found in other plants. An areole is a sharply defined area on a cactus plant from which are produced spines, new joints, flowers, and roots when joints fall to the ground or are transplanted. Areoles are the vital growing areas of cacti.

Cactus flowers have certain characteristics that distinguish them from other flowers. They have an inferior ovary, an abundance of stamens, and numerous sepals and petals with but a slight difference between these two parts of the flower.

As a general statement, the last week in April and the first week in May is a good time to visit cactus land, especially if one is limited to a short vacation period. By consulting the map on page 94, one can pick out as a destination a region on the map which is heavily symboled. There the cacti appear in greater numbers. The flowering season begins in early April with the beaver-tail and is closely followed by the various hedgehog varieties. May brings flowers on the prickly pear, cholla, saguaro, and many of the smaller cacti — this is the time when the greatest number of cactus flowers may be found in Arizona. June presents the stragglers left over from May, and as a special contribution, the flowers of Arizona's Queen of the Night. Fishhook, pincushion, and a few chollas in the higher elevations are in flower during July and August. September finishes the season with the Arizona barrel wearing crowns of yellow, orange, pink, or red flowers. Wet or dry seasons do not affect the blossoming habits of cacti.

It is estimated that there are about 1,600 species of cacti. Of these about 300 are found in the United States; the rest in Mexico, Central America, South America, and neighboring islands. Five unimportant species of the genus *Rhipsalis* are the only members of the cactus family growing native outside the Western Hemisphere. Because they are identical to other members of this genus in Florida and South America and because they were not noted by botanists until the nineteenth century, many authorities believe the *Rhipsales* found in South Africa and Ceylon may have been introduced by man or migratory birds, two ways in which plants can cross oceans.

The approximately 300 species of cacti found in the United States grow mainly in the Southwest. Arizona well deserves the nickname "The Cactus State," having about 72 species of cacti in great abundance native to it. About 200 species are found scattered through Texas, New Mexico, and California, with a few in Nevada and Utah. Only about 10 Arizona cacti, however, are endemic to the state — the rest of them overlap into other states. Cacti travel, and soon make themselves at home in new locations.

The Southwest, then, is truly the domain of the flowering cactus, the logical destination for those lovers of beauty who wish to seek the elegant and the rare in the flowering kingdom when spring grips the land. Here, for all in America to see, is a treasure house of dazzling color and exquisite design. Here is the domain of the flowering cactus.

Saguaro

DESERT MONARCH

*I*n the strange world inhabited by the members of the family Cactaceae (kak-*tay*-cee-ee), none is stranger than the saguaro. Other members of this strange family wander with abandon over the Western Hemisphere, making themselves at home wherever they go. The saguaro (sah-*wah*-ro) has found its natural habitat in southern Arizona. With possible exceptions of a few scattered plants along the Colorado River in southern California and in northern Sonora, Mexico, the saguaro has set up its kingdom in the southern part of America's youngest state.

So typical is it of Arizona that the citizens of the state chose the saguaro blossom as their state flower. A better choice could not have been made. These white, waxy flowers are held like delicate garlands on long, outstretched, and often contorted limbs, flowers unsurpassed for exquisiteness of design.

The saguaro *(Carnegiea gigantea)* is not the largest of the cacti, despite the fact that it is called the giant cactus. Mexico, so rich in so many things, is first in the abundance and diversity of cactus growth, and largest of all is its Pringle cereus *(Pachycereus Pringlei)*, whose majestic proportions exceed those of the saguaro. When the *Pachycereus* appears in colonies one has the feeling of having entered a small forest. When the saguaro appears in colonies one has the feeling of having entered an age and world peopled by weird and ponderous quadrupeds, the kind of creature whose bones, tied together with wire, are focal points of interest in modern museums dedicated to the science of organic evolution.

In the presence of this monarch of the desert, one has a feeling of antiquity. This saguaro, for instance, 50 feet high with limbs extending in all directions, was a healthy youngster when men were penning the first lines of the Constitution and setting up a new nation in a new world. This straight pole, not yet old enough to throw out branching arms, saw the sun rise when Abraham Lincoln was uttering his immortal words at Gettysburg. Phenomenally slow of growth, a mature saguaro will reach an age of a quarter millennium.

The saguaros are the dominant features in the desert landscape. Their sculpturesque forms tower from 40 to 50 feet, sometimes more, above the desert floor. Large forests of these plants grow in southern Arizona at altitudes between 1,000 and 4,000 feet. One such forest of 63,284 acres, near Tucson, has been set aside as the Saguaro National Monument, a protective area to guard the saguaro forever against man and his often destructive civilization.

The plant is a miracle of design with a functional structure unsurpassed in the world of living things. It has a strong supporting cylindrical core of rods extending to its full height, joined by succulent tissue on the inside as well as outside of the core. These dozen or more

NT SAGUARO
negiea gigantea

17

rods, up to 2 inches in diameter, support the tremendous weight of the plant throughout its life, a worthy feat considering that an adult saguaro will weigh as much as 10 to 15 tons.

The plant is covered by parallel flutings, or ridges, converging at the apex. The ridges of the deep flutings are decorated with a network of spine clusters that enclose the dull, green body in a grayish webb, giving a finishing touch

of uniformity to its massive columns. Simplicity of form, well-rounded stem and branches give the saguaro its sculptured appearance.

The saguaro is adapted to the ways of the arid land. It has a widespread, lacy root structure extending far from the plant and near the surface of the ground. Every drop of rainfall is used by the plant. As the root system absorbs moisture the flutings expand with the storing

DETAIL AND HORIZONTAL SECTION OF SAGUARO

of water in the succulent core of the plant. With this storing of water against the dry days that are sure to come in the desert, the plant expands as much as an inch in twenty-four hours. If there have been prolonged rains, new flutings are added to store additional moisture. When the dry days come (a drought of three years has been recorded in the Southwestern desert), the saguaro survives by using its own stored moisture.

It can survive this way for many years.

Spines of two kinds are produced by the plant. For the first sixty or seventy years the juvenile plants bear heavy, reddish-brown spines that eventually weather to a dull black. On reaching maturity, or flowering age, there is a change in the character of the spines. The new growth produces flexible yellowish needlelike bristles, densely felted at the base. Just above the new spine

clusters, the flowers and fruit are borne annually. When the wind is abroad in the desert the spines of the saguaro whistle a tune that rises and falls with the velocity of the wind.

The trunk of the saguaro, covered with a hard, waxy epidermal layer to retain moisture against the demands of the hot sun, generally grows 10 feet or more before branching. Branches or "arms" are nearly vertical. No matter how many arms a plant has, there is always balance and structural symmetry to the design.

Large clusters of white blossoms appear on the extended branches in May and June. The tight, round buds and 3-inch flowers occur singly just above the needlelike spines. The flowers are noted for their numerous pollen-bearing stamens — 3,480 by count in one blossom studied. Like many other members of the cereus group, the flowers of the saguaro open in the late evening and close during mid-morning unless the weather is cool and there is a cloudy sky. Then they remain open until early afternoon. The word "cereus" comes from the Latin, meaning wax-candle, a reference to the candelabra-like branching of some members of the genus.

The egg-shaped fruit, about 3 inches long and half as thick, ripens in late June and July when it splits into two or more segments that curl back, exposing a scarlet lining and small, bright black seeds bedded in a vivid red pulp. Desert birds have no tastier food than this fruit of high sugar

content and slightly acid flavor, and are largely responsible for the distribution of the seeds under palo verde and iron-wood trees where they roost. The undigested seeds falling on the leaf-mold under the trees are protected by dense underbrush while they await the rainy season to germinate. Without the protecting shade of some tree the young saguaros would soon dry up and die. Only a fraction of the seeds germinate under favorable conditions and even fewer reach maturity.

Indians of the Southwest for generations have used the saguaro fruit for the making of preserves and the seeds of the fruit for meal to make cakes. The Papago Indians begin their New Year with the fruiting of the saguaro, and to the Pima Indians the month of July is known as the saguaro harvest moon. Since prehistoric days, desert Indians have called this plant "sah-wah-ro" and have depended on it for food, drink, and building material, and to a great extent still do today.

The numerous round holes up and down the stem and arms are the nesting places of the Gila woodpeckers. The plant lines the excavation with scar tissue, thus providing a cool home inside of the living plant, far above the danger from visiting rodents and snakes. After using its hole one season the woodpecker builds a new nest and the tiny "elf" owl, no larger than a sparrow, takes possession and enjoys a cool home without work or effort on his part.

GIANT SAGU
Carnegiea giga

ORANGE LILY — *Lobivia aurea var. cylindrica*

SNOWBALL CACTUS — *Mammillaria Oliviae.*

GLORY OF TEXAS — *Thelocactus bicolor.*

ENGELMANN'S (STRAWBERRY) HEDGEHOG — *Echinocereus Engelma*

GOLDEN LILY CACTUS — *Lobivia aurea.*

EAGLE CLAWS – *Homalocephala texensis.*

AGHORN CHOLLA – *Opuntia versicolor*

CANE CHOLLA – *Opuntia spinosior.*

LITTLE BARREL — *Sclerocactus Whipplei.*

MEXICAN PINCUSHION — *Mammillaria magnimamma.*

ARIZONA RAINBOW — *Echinocereus pectinatus var. rigidissim*

LACE CACTUS — *Echinocereus pectinatus var. Reichenbachii.*

EASTER LILY CACTUS — *Echinopsis multiplex.*

Queens of the Night

NIGHT-BLOOMING CACTI

*T*here are nearly 450 kinds of night-blooming cacti. They differ in size, shape, and color of the plants and spines, but nearly all have white flowers or white flowers faintly tinged with other colors. Their distributional range includes the West Indies, Florida, and the extreme southern regions of the United States to southeastern California. They grow in abundance in Mexico, Central America, and South America. A popular species of night-blooming cactus is used for hedges in Hawaii. This is the *Hylocereus undatus*, which means "forest cereus that is wavy." It is native to the West Indies and some regions of South America, and was probably introduced to Hawaii by cultivation.

The night-blooming genera include the big columnar giants of Mexico, one of which is the *Pachycereus Pringlei;* the organ-pipe varieties and other members of the cereus family found in the southwestern United States; leafy-type epiphyllums of Central and South America; the small night-blooming hedgehogs of the *Echinopsis* genus in Argentina and Brazil. Each, in its own fashion seeking the sunlight above, has individual characteristics: some are snakelike and coiling; others are vines that wind and twine up the branches of jungle trees, picking up moisture with their aerial roots.

The largest cactus flowers are found among the moon cerei (*Selenicerei*), a group of plants whose stems are vinelike, climbing and trailing. Some are pencil-thin; others are ropelike and coiling, often reaching a length of 20 feet or more. The white flowers appear during May, June, and July and are particularly popular because of their size and beauty.

Most celebrated of the moon cerei is the West Indies' "King of the Night" (*Selenicereus grandiflorus*). The flower forms a cup about 10 inches in diameter and emits a strong vanillalike fragrance. Another noted moon cereus is the "Princess of the Night" (*Selenicereus pteranthus*), native to southern Mexico and Central America, with flowers 12 inches in diameter. Probably the largest of all cactus flowers is "The Queen of the Night" (*Selenicereus Macdonaldiae*), a native of Uruguay and Argentina, commonly found under cultivation in the southwestern United States. The flower is about 13 inches in diameter, with white petals and golden sepals.

A popular collector's item among night-blooming cacti is Mexico's famous snake cactus (*Nyctocereus serpentinus*). The snakelike stems crawl through bushes and over fences and walls, reaching a length of 10 feet or more. The white flowers of this plant appear in May and are about 5 inches in diameter.

The senita or "old one" (*Lophocereus Schottii*), a native of Mexico but found north of the Arizona-Mexico border south of Ajo, Arizona, is characterized by long, bristlelike spines that appear at the top of the stems, resembling gray hair. The very few plants that are found in Arizona are not as large as the Mexi-

ARIZONA QUEEN OF THE NIGHT
eniocereus Greggii

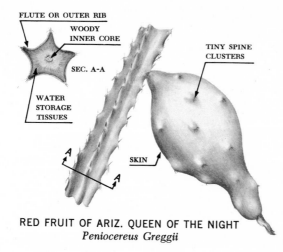

FLUTE OR OUTER RIB
WOODY INNER CORE
SEC. A-A
WATER STORAGE TISSUES
TINY SPINE CLUSTERS
SKIN

RED FRUIT OF ARIZ. QUEEN OF THE NIGHT
Peniocereus Greggii

can variety. Small pinkish flowers appear in May and give off an unpleasant odor during the blooming period at night.

A curious little night-bloomer is the dahlia cactus *(Wilcoxia Diguetii)*. Its root system consists of two or three dozen tan-colored, dahlialike tubers. The whiplike stems and branches above ground are about a quarter inch thick and 4 to 5 feet long. They thread their way through the branches of trees and brush where they are so well concealed that they are very difficult to find. A few specimens have been found along the Mexican border in Yuma and Pima counties of Arizona, but the range of the species is mostly in Sonora, Mexico. The small, white, nocturnal flowers appear in late July.

Arizona's "Queen of the Night" *(Peniocereus Greggii)* or "thread cereus," so called because of the numerous thread-like stamens of its flowers, is one of the loveliest and most celebrated of all night-blooming cacti by reason of its evanescent beauty and spicy fragrance. Its distributional range spreads over most of southern Arizona, to northern Mexico, New Mexico, and west Texas.

A search for this Queen of the Night is a needle-in-the-haystack adventure. It is difficult to find in daylight, for its dried, dead-seeming stick stems blend so well with surrounding vegetation. The plant is easier to find during the flowering season, usually the middle of June, when the pleasant odor of its blooms saturates the air for hundreds of feet around, allowing the plant to be easily traced.

The petals begin to open in a jerky movement soon after sundown. When the flowers are open they measure from 4 to 6 inches in diameter. The inner petals are usually a creamy white, while the sepals may be lavender, purple, brown, or green. In cool weather the plants will bear only a few flowers at a time, but often on a hot night some plants produce twenty to thirty blooms. On an extremely hot day and night the higher temperatures apparently force the underdeveloped buds as well as the mature buds, even on several plants growing in the same vicinity, to open simultaneously. As this happens often in the desert country, this phenomenon has led to the popular belief that all night-blooming cerei bloom the same night. This is true only when exceptionally hot nights occur near the peak of the blooming season.

The blossoms remain open throughout the night. The heavy perfume which saturates the night air attracts insects to the blossoms for pollinization and fertilization of the plants. The flowers close when the sun grows bright in the morning. They last only one night.

The red, egg-shaped fruit ripens in September. Its juicy pulp of high sugar content is used by the Indians for jams and jellies. Dissemination of the species is determined chiefly by the roosting habits of birds who eat the seeds and pulp of the fruit. The birds spread the seeds by droppings in the denser thickets of the desert which is their natural habitat.

The tiny black spines of *Peniocereus Greggii* are arranged in groups of ten or twelve to a cluster, with the clusters lined up like a row of insects along the outer portion of the ribs, and they extend the full length of the stems and branches.

Beneath the shallow root system of the plant is a large tuber that weighs up to 50 pounds. (One such tuber was found to weigh 87 pounds.) This tuber functions as a food and water storage compartment to sustain the plant through long periods of drought. When the frail stems above the ground are broken, new ones are promptly grown from this giant potato-shaped storage reservoir or tuber.

Possibly no cactus is as nondescript during most of the year as the *Peniocereus Greggii*. It compensates for its unattractiveness, however, when it flowers. Then it blazes out in such color and aroma that it is one of the most sought-after and beautiful of all night-blooming cacti.

The "night-blooming cereus" so common in cultivation often is not a cereus but a member of the genus *Epiphyllum*, native to tropical forests of Mexico and South America, where it grows high up on the branches and crotches of jungle trees along with rare orchids. The plants are not parasites but are air plants using the trees solely as a resting place.

SNAKE CACTUS
Nyctocereus serpentinus

ARIZONA QUEEN OF THE NIGHT
Peniocereus Greggii

Organ-pipe

ARISTOCRAT OF THE DESERT

The organ-pipe cactus (*Lemaireocereus Thurberi*) was named in honor of George Thurber, botanist for the Mexican Boundary Commission, one of the first scientists to realize the significance of desert plant life. It is one of the picturesque members of the cactus family. Its regal shape and imposing appearance on the landscape have caused the plant to be referred to as "the aristocrat of cacti."

Native to Lower California and western Sonora, Mexico, it has traveled slowly north until it now occupies a portion of southern Arizona south of Ajo, Arizona. This area has been set aside as the Organ-pipe Cactus National Monument, a vast desert wonderland becoming increasingly popular with students of desert flora and fauna.

The numerous columns of yellow-green stems originate at the base of the organ-pipe cactus, forming large clusters of bristling arms or stems 8 to 15 feet high, resembling from a distance the pipes of a great organ. The cylindrical stems grow from 6 to 8 inches in diameter, their numerous shallow ridges edged with clusters of short, slender, grayish spines that give a slightly velvety look to the columnar stems.

Small, insignificant flowers appear on the organ-pipe cactus, near the tops of the branches, in May and June. Their pale greenish-white petals usually do not open wide. For that reason they lack the showiness of other night-blooming cacti, noted for their vivid blooms.

The plant makes up for the modesty of its blossoms by the richness of its fruit, the most delicious of all cactus fruit. The egg-shaped red fruit, about an inch and a half in diameter, is very spiny, but the spines brush off easily when the fruit is ripe. The fleshy crimson pulp of the fruit is high in sugar content. The Papago Indians, whose reservation adjoins the National Monument, prize the fruit of the organ-pipe cactus and use it to supplement their diet. With the great knowledge of the desert and its plants possessed by these Indians, it is little wonder that they have survived and prospered in a harsh land.

The Mexicans call this plant *pitahaya dulce.* In Sonora, Mexico, where the weather is milder than in Arizona, the plants are less branched and larger than those found north of the border.

The plant is susceptible to frost. Perhaps that is the reason why it has not found its way to the cooler climates of the North. One interesting characteristic of this plant should be noted: while frost may kill a tip of a growing stem or branch, thereby ending its lengthwise growth, the branch will continue to live, gaining in girth throughout its active growing seasons.

In Mexico numerous types of columnar cacti are called "organ-pipe," but *Lemaireocereus marginatus* is the best known because of its use in building fences. Planted side by side the long, slender, durable stems provide privacy.

GAN-PIPE
naireocereus Thurberi

Barrel

TRAVELER'S FRIEND

n this Southwestern solitude the sheer mechanics of living revealed by all desert plants is amazing once it is understood.

Cacti and other desert plants have traveled farthest of all plants along the road of biological adaptation to environment. Of all cacti, the barrel cactus represents the finest example of specialization of which a leafy shoot of a seed is capable.

The barrel cactus is well suited for life in desert regions. The woody core of the stem is from 1 to 3 inches in diameter, although the swollen cortex surrounding it may be several inches thick. The tough, parchmentlike epidermis of the strongly ribbed stem is heavily waxed to prevent the escape of moisture. The dispersement of stout, brightly colored spines further decreases evaporation by cutting off 20 per cent of sunlight and raising the humidity in the shaded area between the surface of the plant and the spines. Here is an admirable example of the cacti's ability to meet the trying conditions the desert presents.

Of the four large barrel cacti native to Arizona, the most conspicuous on the landscape is the Arizona barrel *(Ferocactus Wislizenii)*. The young plants are spherical or nearly so. Mature plants are cylindrical, growing as high as 8 feet and up to 2 feet in diameter. The elongated barrels are often mistaken for young saguaros, although their spines differ greatly as close examination will show.

The flowers of the Arizona barrel, about 3 inches across, range in color from yellow and orange to dark red, and quite often reveal several intermediate shades. The sunlight reflected on the silken petals imparts a metallic sheen to the brightly colored flowers. Arizona barrels generally bloom during July, August, and September.

This plant is also known as the candy barrel and is often used for the making of cactus candy. The implication that the plant has any ingredients suitable for candy is, of course, inaccurate. The succulent white tissue is cut into small squares, boiled in water until tender, drained, boiled in a heavy sugar sirup until the tissue has absorbed the sirup, then each piece is rolled in bar sugar and glazed in the sun. The fleshy tissue contains no sugar and has very little flavor.

Many of the barrel cacti display an abnormal growth of headlike appendages sprouting from the top of the plants. These are the result of injuries probably caused by thirsty natives crushing the top of the plants for the moisture stored in the inner pulp. The sap does not taste bad and can assuage thirst.

The habit of the barrel cacti to lean toward the southwest has earned for them another common name; compass cactus. This leaning is believed to be caused by the more rapid evaporation on the side facing the sun, bringing about a state of "incipient drying" in the walls of the cell tissues. Cell growth is retarded as it loses water faster than it

CALIFORNIA BARREL — *Ferocactus acanthodes*

COVILLE'S BARREL — *Ferocactus Covillei*

BAJA CALIFORNIA BARREL
Ferocactus peninsulae

TOWNSEND'S BARREL
Ferocactus Townsendianus

can absorb it. The faster growth on the less lighted side, or north side, of rigid columnar plants on the desert causes them to orient their growing tips in the general direction of the sun, and the larger barrel cacti to twist in spiral patterns. However, this theory is debatable.

During a rainy season, barrel cacti can absorb and store enough water to last during years of drought. Some of the older plants, when gorged with water during unusually wet periods, topple over from their own excessive weight when the ground becomes so softened from the rain that it cannot hold the plant's roots. Many of these toppled plants continue to live flat on the ground, producing flowers and fruit as if nothing had disturbed their normal life.

The growth of all barrel cacti is very slow and may be completely suspended during years of drought and resumed when rain again falls on the thirsty desert, thereby extending their whole life cycle. For example: the giant barrel (*Echinocactus ingens*) of Mexico grows to a monstrous size, 6 to 9 feet tall, 3 to 4 feet in diameter, weighing several thousand pounds and may attain an estimated age of five to six hundred years. A large healthy barrel accidentally uprooted may take years to die.

There are many barrel cacti growing throughout the Southwest. They are sometimes called the Visnaga or Bisnaga cacti, and they are classified by some scientists under the name *Echinocactus*, a word which is derived from the Greek *echinos* meaning "hedgehog," and *kaktos*, referring to a spiny type of plant.

They are pompous fellows, rather squat and grim in shape with thorny armor, but when they wear their garlands of flowers like gay hats during their flowering season, they can hold their own with the most colorful of all in the flowering desert. The crown of flowers worn by the plant gives it a regal look.

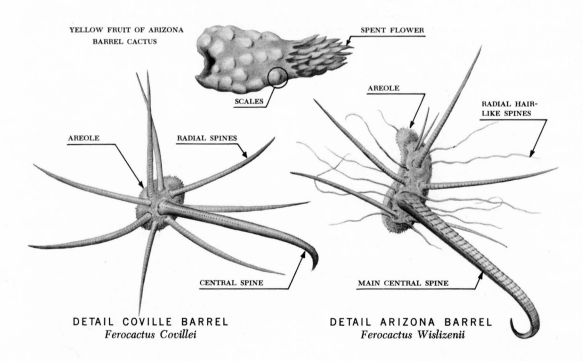

YELLOW FRUIT OF ARIZONA BARREL CACTUS

SPENT FLOWER

SCALES

AREOLE

RADIAL HAIR-LIKE SPINES

AREOLE

RADIAL SPINES

CENTRAL SPINE

MAIN CENTRAL SPINE

DETAIL COVILLE BARREL
Ferocactus Covillei

DETAIL ARIZONA BARREL
Ferocactus Wislizenii

ARIZONA BARR
Ferocactus Wisliz

ORANGE TUNA CACTUS — *Opuntia anacantha.*

ING CHOLLA — *Opuntia Bigelovii.*

ARIZONA BARREL — *Ferocactus Wislizenii.*

BEAVER-TAIL CACTUS — *Opuntia basilaris.*

STAR OF CAPRICORN — *Astrophytum capricorne.*

PRINCESS OF THE NIGHT — *Selenicereus pteranthus.*

RED HEDGEHOG — *Echinocereus triglochidiatus var. melanacanthus.*

TEXAS RAINBOW — *Echinocereus dasyacanthus*

CLARET-CUP CACTUS — *Echinocereus triglochidiat*

PINAL PINCUSHION — *Mammillaria Wilcoxii*

STAGHORN CHOLLA — *Opuntia versicolor.* CANE CHOLLA — *Opuntia spinosior.* CANE CHOLLA — *Opuntia spinosior.*

STAGHORN CHOLLA — *Opuntia versicolor.* STAGHORN CHOLLA — *Opuntia versicolor.* CANE CHOLLA — *Opuntia spinosior.*

ARIZONA PINCUSHION — *Coryphantha vivipara var. arizonica.*

CANE CHOLLA — *Opuntia spinosior.* STAGHORN CHOLLA — *Opuntia versicolor.* STAGHORN CHOLLA — *Opuntia versicolor.*

Cholla

BRISTLING FORTRESS

he term "cholla," meaning head-shaped, is a word of Spanish derivation. The common pronunciation is "choya." In the Southwest the name is applied to the opuntias, distinguished by cylindrical joints, a feature that differentiates them from the flat-jointed opuntias, the prickly pears. Often the crown of a cholla, formed by the branches and joints, is shaped like a human head, which accounts for the name.

There are approximately twenty species of chollas in the southwestern United States. All of them, except for the differences in spines and flowers, could be briefly described as round-jointed cacti whose joints are linked like sausages that range in size from mere pencils on the small plants to hefty rods and antlers on the big trees. One should approach them, if not with temerity, with respect. They are prone to be bad-tempered when molested, and once a careless hand has closed around a joint, or a too-thin-soled shoe has stepped on a joint, the penetrating and stabbing spines will be eloquent evidence that caution is the best course to follow in making an acquaintanceship with these ugly, distorted, but not uninteresting cacti.

The cylindrical joints have tubercles arranged spirally, each bearing an areole which in turn has spines and spicules and also the small greatly reduced fleshy leaves an inch long; these always wither and fall off in less than a week, no doubt remnants from an earlier age when all cacti had leaves. Some cholla spines have thin transparent sheaths, which persist unless destroyed or rubbed off. The barbed and sheathed cholla spines are the most dangerous of all cactus spines. This is an example of plants bearing gorgeous flowers that rate as weeds and pests, because of their aggressive habits. The chollas have never retreated before man, and thrive on trampling by cattle since it gives the broken joints a chance to hitch a ride to new environments where they take root and grow into new plants. Man and his domestic animals fear cholla more than any plant on the desert. However, the cactus wren spends practically its whole life among the cholla branches, where the female builds her nest and rears her young in absolute safety from marauders.

The cane chollas and staghorn chollas (*Opuntia spinosior* and *O. versicolor*) are noted for their grotesque shapes and exquisitely colored flowers that exhibit a mixture of colors blended from different parts of the spectrum, creating a vast symphony of tints and tones. Their dominant colors, red, brown, orange, and yellow, may once have been their only colors but owing, possibly, to cross-pollination they have become mixed into an infinite variety of hues.

There are several intermediate forms between the cane chollas and staghorn chollas — indicating an adjustment of the species to changing environments —

CANE CHOLLA
Opuntia spinosior

which make it difficult to tell one from the other. Both are characterized by their slender, round joints of uneven lengths that branch like the antlers of a deer. The cane cholla *(Opuntia spinosior)* is openly branched with a distinct treelike appearance. Some grow as tall as 10 feet, and bear bright yellow fruit. The staghorn cholla *(Opuntia versicolor)* is more intricately branched, forming denser crowns, and bearing green and purplish fruit. The finely barbed spines of both species are of uneven lengths, varying from one-fourth of an inch to an inch. The lacy inner core, or woody skeleton, of the cane cholla is used by desert craftsmen for furniture, novelties, and picture frames.

In Mexico there is a cholla *(Opuntia imbricata)* from whose fruit is derived an extract that is used in fixing a dye, known in the native arts as cochineal dye. The fruits, after being chopped into small pieces, are boiled, and the seeds filtered out. The extract is used to dissolve and set the cochineal, which is a scarlet dyestuff made from dried female bodies of an insect *(Dactylopius coccus)*, commonly called "cochineal bug." In South America and Mexico, before the introduction of coal-tar dyes, cochineal bugs were grown in large quantities on the cochineal fig-cactus. A weblike mass that may be seen on many of the opuntias indicates the presence of these scarlet insects. The fruits of *Opuntia imbricata* are believed to contain certain salts and organic acids that explain the mordant property of the extract.

In Texas *Opuntia imbricata* is called "candelabrum cactus" because of the arrangement of its branches in the manner of a giant, ornamental candlestick. Its specific name *"imbricata"* means overlapping, like shingles, and refers to the overlapping tubercles that almost cover the surface of the joints, somewhat like roofing tiles. Each tubercle bears a set of short spines that are covered with loose-fitting, varicolored sheaths. This cholla bears a close resemblance to the cane cholla *(Opuntia spinosior)* and is treelike in form, from 3 to 8 feet tall. The lacy, wooden skeleton, like that of

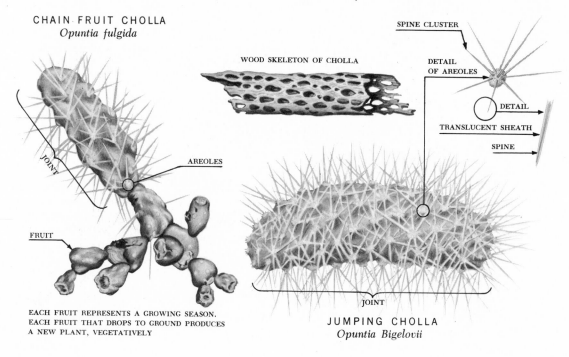

CHAIN FRUIT CHOLLA
Opuntia fulgida

WOOD SKELETON OF CHOLLA

SPINE CLUSTER

DETAIL OF AREOLES

DETAIL

TRANSLUCENT SHEATH

SPINE

JOINT

AREOLES

FRUIT

EACH FRUIT REPRESENTS A GROWING SEASON.
EACH FRUIT THAT DROPS TO GROUND PRODUCES
A NEW PLANT, VEGETATIVELY

JOINT

JUMPING CHOLLA
Opuntia Bigelovii

the cane cholla, is used in the manufacture of novelty furniture and picture frames. The flowers are red or purple and occur during June and July — rarely in May or August. The candelabrum cholla is widely distributed and consists of several racial phases or geographical variations, spreading from central Mexico through western Texas and New Mexico to central Colorado.

Most attractive of the opuntias is the jumping cholla *(Opuntia Bigelovii)*. Because of its formidable armament of spines and readily detached joints, this is the most dangerous cactus that man or animal can encounter on the desert. The jumping cholla spines will penetrate the toughest hide of an animal at the least touch. But the kangaroo rat uses the fallen joints to build his home. Hundreds of vicious cholla joints are used in lining the maze of runways under the mound of debris he collects for his home. Some of these piles are stacked 3 to 4 feet high and 7 to 8 feet across, with the entrances to the runways barely wide enough for the rodent to enter.

No coyote would be rash or foolish enough to dig for a meal in this spiny fortress. How the kangaroo rat accomplishes this feat without injury is one of the mysteries of the desert.

It is from the fact that densely spiny joints attach themselves at the slightest touch to the flesh of the intruder that the plant receives its colloquial name. Yet the glittering gold and silvery spines add much to the plant's attractiveness.

A jumping cholla's habit of dropping its joints, more noticeable during a prolonged drought than at other times, seems to have as its object the conservation of moisture within the plant and the plant's desire to reproduce vegetatively. The ground under a jumping cholla is littered with spiny joints, waiting for the rains that will bring them an opportunity to take root and grow. This vegetative method of propagation would naturally result in few variations; therefore, flower colors of jumping chollas are nearly the same throughout the species; whitish with green centers. The plants are more or less alike in every respect.

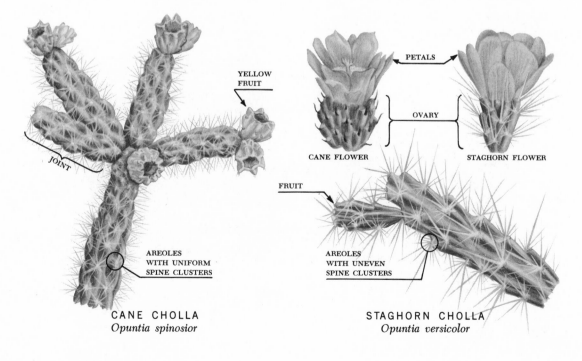

CANE CHOLLA
Opuntia spinosior

STAGHORN CHOLLA
Opuntia versicolor

CHAIN-FRUIT CHOLLA — *Opuntia fulgida*

CANE CHOLLA — *Opuntia spinosior*

MPING CHOLLA
puntia Bigelovii

Travelers in the Southwest occasionally come upon plantations of large, treelike plants whose drooping joints are weighted down with chains of green fruit. Some of these plants grow as high as 12 feet. They are branched in the manner of a candelabra, with each branch topped by a harum-scarum arrangement of small branches and joints. These are the chain-fruit chollas whose fruits display a strange habit of growth whereby new fruits and flowers grow out from the tips of old fruits. In this manner a chain of ten or twelve fruits is formed that remains on the plant for several years, all fresh and firm. The first fruits, ten or twelve years older than the last, grow slightly larger and firmer than the later fruits, but no less succulent. Fruits that finally do fall to the ground develop roots, the same as the spiny joints, then grow into new plants. Seeds within the fruits seldom have a chance to germinate, though viable and capable of growth. Because of their easily dislodged spiny joints chain-fruit chollas are also called by some "jumping cactus." The shining needlelike spines that cover the joints gleam like tiny icicles in the sunlight, from which characteristic is derived the plant's botanical name, *Opuntia fulgida*. The inconspicuous flowers of this plant may be white, pink, or lavender.

One of the most insignificant members of the cholla group of cacti is the "ramose" cholla (*Opuntia ramosissima*). Most of its kind are seldom over 3 feet high, although there are a few plants that reach a height of 6 feet in the most favored localities of its growing range, which extends from southeast Nevada, south through eastern California and western Arizona into northern Sonora,

Mexico. This bushlike cactus is very much branched (a characteristic that accounts for its common and specific name) in an intricately crisscross arrangement of its pencillike joints. The lack of eye appeal in this plant is somewhat compensated for by the tiny armorlike plates, of great botanical interest, that cover the joints and branches. Each of the plates, or diamond-shaped shields, bears an areole that produces one needlelike spine about 2 inches long. Each spine is covered by a yellow papery sheath. All the areoles grow whitish wool and numerous tiny barbed glochids. Because of the small plates, or shields, a ramose cholla gives the appearance of a plant that is protected by chain armor — and woe to the hand that touches it. The flowers of the ramose cholla are even less attractive than the plant. They are about a half-inch in diameter and an insipid greenish-yellow in color. Despite the poor showing this cactus makes on the desert landscape some cactus growers in the Southwest feel that no cactus garden is complete without it, and it is, no doubt, a practical plant for a small garden because it takes up very little room and does not spread rapidly like some larger and faster-growing chollas.

The devil cholla (*Opuntia Stanlyi*) is well named. This crawling mass of prostrate stems, less than a foot high, forms impenetrable patches often 20 feet across. The large clusters of daggerlike spines are dangerous and effectively repulse the advances of any animal or human foolish enough to invade its territory. The small pale yellow flowers are inconspicuous and lack the flamboyance of the cane or staghorn chollas. This species can hardly be called "attractive" and is of interest only as a botanical study.

CANE CHOLL
Opuntia spinos

COMB CACTUS — *Echinocereus pectinatus var. caespitosus.*

STAR CACTUS — *Astrophytum myriostigma.*

PURPLE PRICKLY PEAR — *Opuntia Santa-R*

SAND DOLLAR — *Astrophytum asterias.*

DEVIL'S FINGER — *Echinocereus Blanckii.*

PEANUT CACTUS — *Chamaecereus Silvestri.*

COMMON PINCUSHION — *Coryphantha vivipara var. aggregata.*

MIDNIGHT LADY — *Eriocereus Bonpland*

PORCUPINE CACTUS — *Opuntia erinacea var. hystricina.*

MILLER'S PINCUSHION — *Mammillaria microcarpa var. Milleri.*

CANE CHOLLA — *Opuntia spinosior.*

URPLE HEDGEHOG — *Echinocereus Fendleri var. Bonkerae.*

STAGHORN CHOLLA — *Opuntia versicolor.*

SUN GODDESS ORCHID CACTUS — *Epiphyllum* hybrid

MARSEILLAISE ORCHID CACTUS — *Epiphyllum* hybrid

UPREME ORCHID CACTUS — *Epiphyllum* hybrid

CONWAY GIANT ORCHID CACTUS — *Epiphyllum* hybrid

CELESTINE ORCHID CACTUS — *Epiphyllum* hybrid

FENDLER'S HEDGEHOG — *Echinocereus Fendleri.*

GREEN SIRENS — *Eriocereus pomanensis.*

E EMPRESS — *Nopalxochia phyllanthoides.*

BLUE CEREUS — *Cereus hexagonus.*

PANCAKE PRICKLY PEAR — *Opuntia chlorotica.*

Pincushion and Fishhook

BABY CACTI

visitor to the flowering desert for the first time soon makes an acquaintance with the saguaro, organ-pipe, cholla, and barrel because appearances and unique personalities are individually impressive on first meeting. By their very size they usually dominate that part of the landscape in which they find themselves.

Size is not the only yardstick by which one can measure the interest-provoking qualities of cactus plants. The unobservant or the hurried will miss much of the strange and the beautiful that exist along desert trails by overlooking the smaller members of the clan — the pincushions and the fishhooks — simply because their diminutive stature does not call attention to them. One must be wise in desert ways to find these small cacti in their off-blossoming season. They conceal themselves well among other desert plants. Even the most prepossessing in appearance of these particular species are hard to tell normally from small, gray rocks, but when they send forth their flowers, often as large as themselves, they are just as colorful and as flamboyant as any cactus.

A pincushion cactus is any small globular or cylindrical cactus having numerous pinlike spines. Some, whose spines are hooked at the ends, are also called "fishhook cacti." There are hundreds of different kinds. They are so numerous and so distantly related that botanists have divided them into several groups, or genera, the largest of which is the genus *Mammillaria*. This genus includes about 200 species, three-fourths of which are native to Mexico. About seventeen species are native to the southwestern United States. A few species have been found in Venezuela.

One of the most prominent and showiest of this branch of the cactus family is *Mammillaria microcarpa*. Little candy-striped flowers of lavender, red, or pink form a circle near the top of the stems in April and, again, in July and August — as a general rule — but some years in some regions of the desert they begin to bloom halfheartedly in February, in others they bloom from April to October. The cylindrical stems, about 4 inches in height, are studded with nipplelike tubercles, or *mammillae;* hence the group name. At the tips of the tubercles are borne the spines that radiate like the spokes in a wheel, but sometimes form starlike clusters. Often the spines are so numerous and interlaced that they obliterate the stems. The plants sometimes consist of three or more stems, but generally only one. On the desert they usually grow close to larger plants and are difficult to find except when they are in flower.

Other species of *Mammillaria* are globular and form mounds, because of the offshoots and branches. Some, like *Mammillaria Heyderi*, the cream cactus, or Heyder's pincushion, are normally single-stemmed and flat like a half-globe. The cream cactus derives its name from its characteristic milky, latex - like sap.

Coryphantha, which means "top-flowering," is another group of the pincushions, consisting of some fifty species. They, too, are common in Mexico, about forty-five species in all, although about ten species have spread north into the southwestern United States. One species, *Coryphantha vivipara*, is native to nearly all the western states and Manitoba and Alberta, Canada.

The two most common pincushions in this group are *Coryphantha vivipara var. aggregata*, or "common pincushion cactus,"— sometimes called "rising biscuits" — and *Coryphantha vivipara var. arizonica*, or Arizona pincushion cactus. The stems of the rising biscuits usually flatten out in winter from dehydration, but after the rains in spring they swell and rise into a mound of small globes, a characteristic from which they derive their colloquial name. Their globular stems are studded with tubercles spirally arranged, each bearing clusters of thirty to forty needlelike spines that completely hide the plant body. Their lavender and pink flowers appear in late May and June. They are common to Arizona, New Mexico, and Sonora, Mexico.

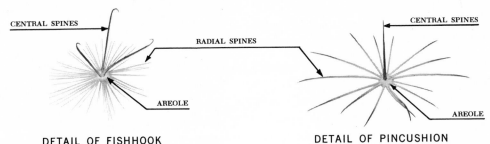

DETAIL OF FISHHOOK

DETAIL OF PINCUSHION

CALIFORNIA FISHHOOK
Mammillaria tetrancistra

MISSOURI PINCUSHION
Neobesseya Missouriensis

Prickly Pear

GYPSY OF THE CLAN

early everyone is familiar with at least one of the 150-odd species of prickly pears. They have spread out from Mexico, their classical home, to southern Canada, from coast to coast, and to every state in the United States except Maine, New Hampshire, and Vermont. They have traveled south to the Straits of Magellan and have taken to the wilds and prospered where there is sunshine and sand to bring their particular virtues into play. They are the gypsies of the cactus tribe.

In order to gain a foothold in the various regions they have invaded, each type of prickly pear has developed its own peculiarities. Some have spines to break the heat or cold, while others are spineless with a tough leathery hide. Still others are protected by a dense covering of long white hair instead of spines. There are large treelike forms, mostly in the hot regions, and tiny ground creepers in the cold climates. When winter sets in they can dehydrate their pads to prevent freezing or in desert regions they can hold water through long periods of drought. They readily adapt themselves to the environment wherever they happen to be.

With very few exceptions the flowers of the prickly-pear cacti are yellow; at least they are in the morning when they first open. But in the desert, in the heat of the sun which changes the pigments, they turn darker throughout the day to a burnt-orange, brown, or red. They last for a day only, except when they are brought indoors upon a detached flowering pad where they will last for two or three days. As a matter of fact, all day-blooming cacti will bloom continuously and longer indoors under fluorescent lights than in the broiling summer sun. Cactus flowers appearing in early, cool spring weather last for two to five days. It is the heat of an early summer that wilts a blossom in a day.

The life span of the prickly pear is the shortest of all cacti—not over twenty years. This is compensated by their rapid reproduction, both vegetatively and by seeds. When a plant has exhausted its growing energies the joints break off. Some rot, but most fall to the ground, sprout roots, and grow. This results in a progressive multiplication of their numbers. By this process of division and multiplication the prickly pear species have traveled farther over the Western Hemisphere than any other cacti. In a few places they have become pests, as in Australia, where they escaped from cultivation. In Palestine and other places along the shores of the Mediterranean, where they were introduced into cultivation, they have become a characteristic feature of the landscape.

The prickly pears are abundant in the Southwest. Some of them, such as the grizzly-bear and porcupine cacti, are highly prized by collectors. The most common, though, is the Engelmann's prickly pear (*Opuntia Engelmannii*), named in honor of Dr. George Engel-

ENGELMANN'S (COMMON) PRICKLY PEAR — *Opuntia Engelmannii*

PRICKLY PEAR FRUIT — *Opuntia flavescens*

ALL HOME GARDEN IN THE SOUTHWEST
CKLY PEARS LEFT AND RIGHT

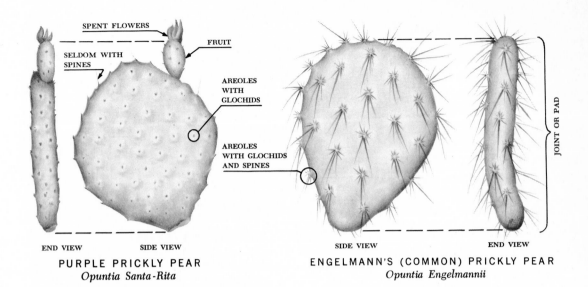

SPENT FLOWERS

FRUIT

SELDOM WITH SPINES

AREOLES WITH GLOCHIDS

AREOLES WITH GLOCHIDS AND SPINES

JOINT OR PAD

END VIEW   SIDE VIEW

PURPLE PRICKLY PEAR
Opuntia Santa-Rita

SIDE VIEW   END VIEW

ENGELMANN'S (COMMON) PRICKLY PEAR
Opuntia Engelmannii

mann, the noted botanist who first described most of the Southwest's cacti. In places favorable to their growth large plants are grouped into colonies, sometimes 150 feet wide, and they grow in plantations as far as one can see. The tulip prickly pear *(Opuntia phaeacantha)* has spread more widely over the Southwest than Engelmann's prickly pear, but it is mostly low-growing and creeping, and for that reason does not make much of an impression on the landscape.

The fruit of Engelmann's prickly pear becomes reddish-purple in color when ripe, appearing in a row along the upper edges of the pads. A plant in full fruit is very attractive. Moreover, the fruit, when peeled, is tasty and nutritious. Not all cactus fruit is edible. Some species produce only dry fruit without pulp. The edible fruit has a juicy pulp in which the small seeds are imbedded.

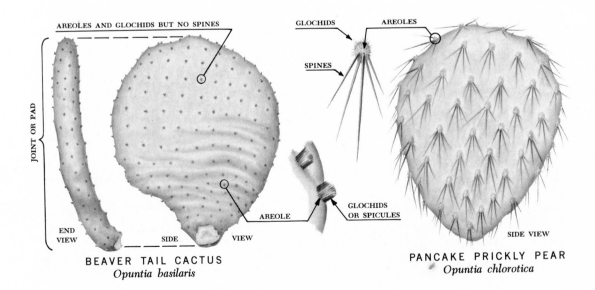

AREOLES AND GLOCHIDS BUT NO SPINES

GLOCHIDS   AREOLES

SPINES

JOINT OR PAD

END VIEW   SIDE   VIEW

AREOLE

GLOCHIDS OR SPICULES

SIDE VIEW

BEAVER TAIL CACTUS
Opuntia basilaris

PANCAKE PRICKLY PEAR
Opuntia chlorotica

Hedgehog

DESERT SURPRISE

*T*he term "hedgehog" is a common name for all the members of the genus *Echinocereus;* a name derived from the Greek *echinos*, meaning hedgehog, and the Latin *cereus*, meaning wax candle. However, the name hedgehog is not commonly confined to any one genus. Generally speaking, any low-growing cactus whose stem is columnar, ribbed, and spiny is called a hedgehog cactus.

The hedgehogs in the *Echinocereus* group are all low, columnar plants whose stems are from 3 to 12 inches high. Of the seventy-five species of this group that have been classified, twenty-seven are native to the western United States. A few grow as far north as Wyoming.

The most prominent of all hedgehogs found in the Southwest is Engelmann's hedgehog or strawberry hedgehog *(Echinocereus Engelmannii)*, a shaggy little plant because of its drooping, needlelike spines, 1 to 5 inches long, that densely cover the stems. Flowers, either purple or pink, appear in late March and April, growing from the sides and near the top of the stems, which occur in clusters of two to twenty-five to a plant.

Fendler's hedgehog *(Echinocereus Fendleri)* has shorter and fewer spines than Engelmann's hedgehog, revealing more of the dark green stem, which is also shorter than that of Engelmann's hedgehog and more oval in shape. There are four variant forms of *Echinocereus Fendleri* — in addition to the typical form — but all of them can be briefly described as erect, spiny cucumbers, one or several to a plant. The flowers, often lasting four days, appear from late March to early May. They are purple, red, or pink.

The red hedgehog — sometimes called "crimson hedgehog" — *(Echinocereus*

NIGHT-BLOOMING HEDGEHOG
Echinopsis hybrid

SPIRAL HEDGEHOG
Hamatocactus setispinus

triglochidiatus var. melanacanthus) is often found growing in mounds of a hundred stems or more, as wide as 4 feet and a foot high. As many as sixty-five crimson blossoms have been counted on one plant, making a very showy dis-

RED FRUIT OF STRAWBERRY HEDGEHOG
Echinocereus Engelmannii

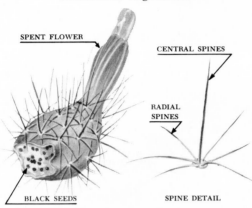

SPENT FLOWER

CENTRAL SPINES

RADIAL SPINES

BLACK SEEDS

SPINE DETAIL

YELLOW HEDGEHOG
Echinocereus subinermis

play on a drab hillside. The red hedgehog prefers the higher elevations of the Southwest.

The claret-cup cactus *(Echinocereus triglochidiatus)* is, typically, a New Mexico species, but is also found in southwest Texas and along the eastern border of Arizona. The soft, fleshy stems are often found arranged by the hundreds in great plant clumps, as wide as 5 feet across. The claret-cup resembles the red hedgehog *(Echinocereus triglochidiatus var. melanacanthus)* but has fewer and stouter spines, fewer and broader ribs. The claret-red flowers occur during April, May, and June — depending upon the altitude — and last several days, possibly because they seek out the higher elevations where the sun is not so severe as in the desert.

The Arizona rainbow cactus *(Echinocereus pectinatus var. rigidissimus)* is a single-stem plant 3 to 4 inches in diameter and up to 12 inches high. It is completely covered with short, stiff spines, pressed flat against the stem. The spines are arranged in alternately colored bands around the stem, red, yellow, and white, from which characteristic the plant derives its common name, which is both accurate and descriptive. The attractive reddish flowers appear in May.

The hedgehogs are small, and although they are widely scattered from western Texas to California, from Sonora, Mexico, to southern Utah and southern Nevada, they, like all the small cacti, do not occupy an important part of the desert adventure until they bloom. When they do, they make up for their size by vivid coloring of their blooms. They are among the most popular plants for southwestern cactus gardens because of their size and free flowering habits.

THOMPSON HEDGE
Echinocereus Fendleri var. Boyce-Thomp.

PURPLE PRICKLY PEAR — *Opuntia Santa-Rita*

ENGELMANN'S (COMMON) PRICKLY PEAR — *Opuntia Engelma*

ENGELMANN'S (STRAWBERRY) HEDGEHOG — *Echinocereus Engelmannii.*

Orchid

PRIZE FOR THE COLLECTOR

ew plants cultivated for their flowers can excel the large, richly colored blossoms of the orchid cacti (*Epiphyllum* hybrids), products of the hybridist's skill. Their wide range in color and long-lasting flowers, together with their easy culture, make them very desirable house plants.

The first hybrids were developed in Europe over a century ago, far from the natural habitat of cacti. Early maritime traders brought strange plants to Europe from Mexican and South American ports; among them were the epiphytes (air plants growing upon other plants but not parasitic) *Nopalxochia phyllanthoides* with small, pink, long-lasting flowers, and the terrestrial *Heliocereus speciosus*, a day-blooming carmine-flowered variety with a beautiful iridescent blue sheen. These soon found their way into the hands of collectors, who were shortly applying the new art of hybridizing. The ease in crossing these two plants led to many fine hybrids.

Less than thirty years ago H. M. Wegener of Los Angeles, California, imported some of the European hybrid cacti. He crossed them with native true species and built up, within ten years, an outstanding collection of several hundred kinds. Other growers soon became enthusiastic over the "new" cactus plants, and lost no time in producing several thousand varieties that for sheer beauty of flower and wide range of colors cannot be surpassed by any other plant, except perhaps by a small number of rare orchids that must be cultivated in special glass houses at great expense.

Like all members of the cactus family, the hybrid orchid cacti are drought-resisting. The long, green, leaflike joints often grow round and woody for a few inches before flattening or becoming three-winged. The body of the joint consists of water-storing tissue and a woody core. The rounded crenations in which the areoles sit are alternately notched. Aerial roots often develop on the tips and along the midrib of the leaflike joints; these take moisture from the humid air and are remnants of their ancestors.

The hybrid orchid cacti may be planted in glazed colored pots or hanging baskets. The rooted or unrooted cuttings or joints cost very little and have the advantage of growing into plants shaped to suit the individual. The plant form is bushlike, branching from the base with long drooping branches suitable for hanging baskets. If a bushy plant is desired, the branches are pinched back; that is, the growing tip is cut off with the fingernails when it reaches the desired length. This makes an ideal pot plant.

Because of their limited root system, a rich soil is necessary to give them sufficient nourishment for growth and flowering. One of the best mixtures for orchid cacti is made by using one part oak leafmold, one part coarse gravel, one part well-rotted cow manure, and one part

THUNDER CLOUD ORCHID CACTUS
Epiphyllum hybrid

rich garden soil. To this may be added a tablespoonful of crushed charcoal for each pot, to keep the soil sweet. The resulting mixture will be permeable, air-containing, nourishing but not heavy. Success depends in no small measure on the exact observance of a definite formula of soil mixture. Any good nourishing soil such as is commonly used for ferns or begonias may be used with fair success.

For potting rooted cuttings and re-potting plants, it is necessary for the quick drainage of surplus water to place a layer of coarse gravel or pieces of crushed clay pots at the bottom of the container. Hold the cutting or plant being potted suspended in proper growing position in the pot and fill in around the roots with the premixed soil formula.

Press the soil gently but firmly around the base of the plant, being careful not to break the roots. Withhold water for a week, then water sparingly until the plant is reestablished.

Unrooted cuttings should be placed in a cool, shady place for a week or ten days, or until the cut portion has formed scar tissue. A small flat should be filled with equal parts of peat moss and coarse sand, in which the cuttings should be planted to a depth of 1½ inches and water withheld for three or four days; then keep the soil barely moist until they show signs of new growth, after which they may be transplanted to small pots.

The hybrid orchid cacti need very little sun, but must have plenty of light and fresh air. In cool, moist climates they do well on a shady porch where they are

WINDOW DISPLAY OF ORCHID CACTI — *Epiphyllum* hybrid

sheltered from hard rains and receive the slanting rays of the morning or evening sun. Plants should be watered daily during the hot weather, but only enough water to keep the soil moist — never sodden. In winter they may be stored in a cool room with a temperature of not under 35° and not over 50° at most, as a higher temperature may induce new growth during their resting period and result in few if any flowers the following spring. During the winter months water should be decreased to a half cup once a week, or just enough to keep plants healthy. Water may be increased in early March when buds make their appearance. After the buds are set and during the growing season, additional food should be provided by using a top dressing of cow manure or a good commercial plant food used according to directions.

A fine spraying of the branches once or twice a month not only removes accumulated dust but is beneficial to the health of the plant.

Orchid cacti grow well on their own roots, but grafting forces growth, earlier maturity, and flowers. When small cuttings are grafted on fast growing stock, such as *Eriocereus* or the less spiny *Opuntia* pads, they take on the vigor and hardiness of the stock. One of the simplest methods of grafting is to slit the top of an *Opuntia* pad with a sharp knife and insert the beveled end of the cutting or scion into the stock and pin it in place with a cactus spine. Grafting stock requires sufficient plant food to maintain the requirements of the graft or the stock will wither in a short time.

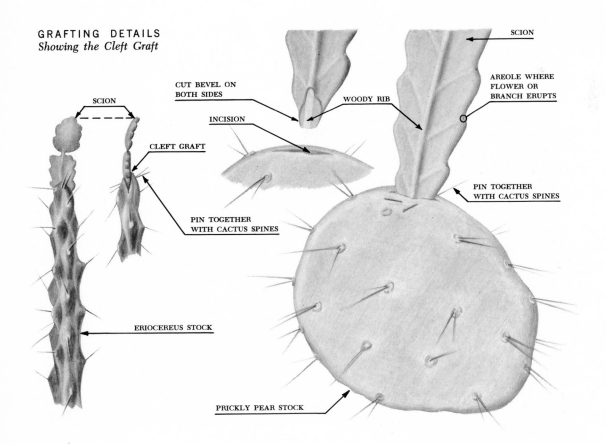

GRAFTING DETAILS
Showing the Cleft Graft

SCION

CUT BEVEL ON BOTH SIDES

INCISION

CLEFT GRAFT

SCION

PIN TOGETHER WITH CACTUS SPINES

WOODY RIB

SCION

AREOLE WHERE FLOWER OR BRANCH ERUPTS

PIN TOGETHER WITH CACTUS SPINES

ERIOCEREUS STOCK

PRICKLY PEAR STOCK

Cultivation

OF DESERT CACTI

Collecting and growing desert cacti for their strange forms and exquisite flowers requires little effort and attention. Amateur gardeners usually kill their plants with too much pampering and overwatering. The theory that if a little water will make a plant grow, more water should do a faster job, may work with other plants but not with cacti. After centuries of adapting themselves to living in arid regions, most cacti now prefer and must have waterless periods to use up the moisture stored in their tissue, or death results.

A porous soil is an absolute necessity — one that drains off surplus water quickly, yet does not dry out too rapidly. A good soil mixture for desert cacti is obtained by mixing equal parts of rich garden soil and coarse gravel, adding a tablespoonful of crushed charcoal and one of hydrated lime. Powdered egg-shells may be substituted for the lime.

One of the most-ignored rules in planting cacti is that roots must be trimmed back short, leaving only three or four short stubs to hold the plant in position. After trimming the roots back, allow them to heal over for a few days before planting. Experience will prove that cacti reestablish themselves sooner if they grow a new set of roots. Unrooted cacti and cuttings will grow roots when placed in a flat of moist sand.

Either clay or glazed pots a little larger than the plant's circumference — including the spines — are suitable. A handful of coarse gravel or broken clay pots should be placed at the bottom, followed by the soil mixture filled to about 2 inches from the top, leaving a cone shaped hollow in the center. Hold the cactus with tongs in the proper growing position over the hollow and fill in with clean, coarse sand. A thin layer of loose

HOW TO POT A NEWLY ACQUIRED CACTUS

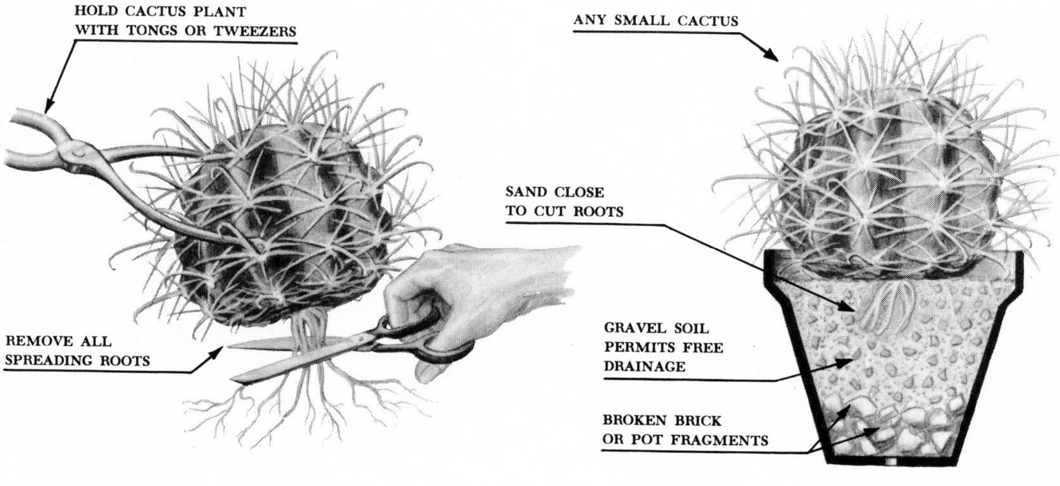

HOLD CACTUS PLANT WITH TONGS OR TWEEZERS

REMOVE ALL SPREADING ROOTS

ANY SMALL CACTUS

SAND CLOSE TO CUT ROOTS

GRAVEL SOIL PERMITS FREE DRAINAGE

BROKEN BRICK OR POT FRAGMENTS

gravel at the top prevents the soil from washing away when the plants are watered.

Newly potted plants should be watered sparingly for three or four weeks, not more than a half cup of water once a week. After the plants are established they should receive a thorough soaking twice a month during hot weather. If cacti are very small, a little water may be applied every few days as they need it. A small drink or two during the winter months keeps the inactive roots from drying up. Water should be increased in spring when signs of new growth appear. At all times water cacti according to the individual needs of the plants. A potted plant on the window sill dries out faster than the same plant growing in a garden. Always allow the soil to become nearly dry before watering again.

Dish gardens must always be regarded as floral arrangements and not as permanent plantings. Since there are no drainage holes in dish gardens the small cacti must be watered sparingly with a syringe.

Sunshine and fresh air are essential for healthy plants. Maximum sunshine is obtained in a window having a southern exposure, or a sunny porch where they are sheltered from the hard rains. In the Southwest the desert-type cacti are grown outdoors, but those native to semiarid regions of Mexico and South America are given lath-house protection from the hot desert sun, and an extra drink of water occasionally.

All varieties of cacti may be planted at any time of the year without injury. If planted during the winter months, a plant should not be watered until spring growth appears; a necessary precaution against decay of dormant roots.

WINDOW DISPLAY OF
CACTI AND DISH GARDEN

GRAFTED GOLDEN BALL CACTUS
Notocactus Leninghausii

Photography
CAPTURING BEAUTY ON FILM

Capturing some of the ever-changing color phases in cactus flowers can be the highlight in anyone's desert adventure. The difficult problem in cactus photography is being at the right place at the right time for the most photogenic flower arrangements.

To set down a hard-and-fast set of rules to guide a photographer seeking portraits of the flowering cactus is not easy to do. Cacti are scattered over a wide variety of habitats where climatic conditions vary considerably with the elevations, thereby causing different flowering seasons at different places.

The southeast quarter of Arizona can boast of more cactus flowers during April and May than any other region of the Southwest. But the tourist photographer on a quick vacation would do well to explore the region around Tucson, Arizona, in *late April and early May*. Here — and usually at this time — several varieties of cacti are in flower. These include the saguaro, purple prickly pear, common prickly pear, and cane cholla. The cane cholla alone presents hundreds of distinctly different color designs.

Most day-blooming cactus flowers are fully open between eleven o'clock in the morning and three o'clock in the afternoon; a time, unfortunately, when light is poorest for plant and habitat views. But this presents no lighting problem for flower close-ups because the same dramatic effect that is provided by early morning and late afternoon crosslighting can be attained under the vertical rays of the midday sun, simply by maneuvering the camera into a position where its back does not face the sun, so that the lens can be directed upon the flower from the side angle. Cactus plants can be photographed to good advantage later in the afternoon when the light is best suited for landscapes. The flowers at that time may be in an advanced stage of closing but the colorful outer petals will be conspicuous in the afternoon sunlight and give a good account of themselves in the developed film.

The eye appeal of a flower close-up can be greatly enhanced by placing or holding a colored matboard behind the flowers that appear in the view finder so that all distracting matter that cannot be brought into focus will be eliminated from the picture. Matboards can be purchased at paint and art stores. Black is effective as a night scene and renders photography of nocturnal flowers simple in the early morning sunlight. This is how Arizona's Queen of the Night on page 28 was photographed at seven o'clock in the morning before the flowers began to close. However, most cactus flowers, particularly when they occur in large clusters, present a striking picture in their natural setting.

The operation of a camera and the factors that determine a good exposure technique are problems that any beginner in the field of photography can work out according to his own requirements after a careful study of the manufactur-

TYPICAL SET-UP FOR
SAGUARO FLOWER CLOSE-UP

er's instructions that come with the equipment he happens to choose. A light meter and tripod, if extreme close-ups are desired, are essential.

The color close-ups in this book were made with a 3¼ x 4¼ inch Speed Graphic camera using an f/4.5 Rodenstock-Trinar-anastigmat (noncoated) lens, mounted in Compur shutter. A tripod and a model 650 Weston light meter were also used. The light meter was set, on an average, at one-half the manufacturer's recommended film speed — which is "8" for 3¼ x 4¼ inch Ektachrome sheet film — because less light reaches the film according to the *length* of the bellows, which becomes greater as the camera is moved closer to the subject to be photographed, necessitating relatively long exposures at small diaphragm apertures. Because of the extremely close range between the lens and the flowers the exposures were calculated on the bases of film speeds of 3 - 4 - 5 in sunlight of 400 according to the light meter, and the pictures were thus taken at diaphragm-click-stops of f/18. at 1/5 sec., f/32. at 1/2 sec., or f/16. at 1/10 sec. The plant habitat views, since they did not require extending the camera bellows, were simple long shots. The diaphragm-click-stops by which these were photographed were, on the average, f/12.7 at 1/25 sec., and f/9. at 1/50 sec., and were calculated on the basis of the normal film speed of "8" by a meter reading at the usual 400 in the desert sunlight which is constant from 7 A.M. until 4 P.M. — except during cloudy weather. One number 4 photoflood lamp was used to illuminate the night-blooming cactus flowers that are grown in gardens, that close before sunrise. Artificial light type color film was used, which is also rated

at a normal speed of "8." With the light placed at a side angle about 6 feet from the flowers, the exposures were calculated on the basis of a film speed of "4" with the camera lens about 18 inches away and a light reading of 50. The resulting diaphragm-click-stops were, on the average, f/16. at 1 sec., or f/11. at 1/2 sec. Photoflash lights were not used, although they are a great help to some photographers who photograph flowers on the desert at night. By this method of illumination it is very difficult to capture the delicate tones in cactus flowers. Sunlight, whenever possible, gives the best results.

The easiest way to photograph cactus flowers is with the use of that popular instrument, the mighty miniature camera. Lithographers are warming up more and more to 35-mm film, especially for processing the small plates such as the quarter-page size herein. Up to 3½ feet from the subject the miniature camera can capture on film close-in cactus plants loaded with flowers. Large clusters of cactus flowers can be found that will fill up the film for a close-up effect without the bother of making corrections for the loss of the film speed that is encountered with the use of a large camera with an extension bellows. The miniature has the advantage of speed that will allow for short exposures under conditions when speed is needed most. With the use of supplementary lenses *extreme* close-ups just as good as the ones in this book are possible if the manufacturer's instructions are carefully studied. They function on the same principle as the well-known portrait attachment. Eastman Kodak Company and E. Leitz, Inc., both produce lenses for this purpose. The Eastman types are sold under the trade name Kodak Portra Lenses. They are 1+, 2+, and 3+ positive lenses of 1, 2, and 3 diopters. They may be used in front of any camera lens singly or in combination, depending upon how close a range the photographer desires to focus. The strongest of the Portra lenses makes possible a 13-inch focusing range on a field size approximately 6 x 9 inches, and field sizes down to about 3¼ x 4¾ inches are possible by a combination of the Portra lenses.

Portra lenses present no focusing problems when used on some types of reflex cameras because the flowers can be focused sharply upon their ground-glass screen if it is designed for direct focusing. But in the case of a camera whose view finder works separate from the taking lens, flowers may be cut off on the side or top corresponding to the view finder's position relative to the taking lens. This problem can be easily solved by the use of one of the standard-make copy attachments.

The Joshua-tree forest, about 15 miles northwest of Congress, Arizona, is a scenic habitat for beaver-tail cacti, where nearby mountain ranges provide a beautiful background for an inspiring cactus-habitat view. Here there is an abundance of exceptionally wide plant clumps that are adorned in *mid-April* with hundreds of rose-red and pink flowers. This is an ideal situation for perfect pictures by the use of a hand-held camera of the box or folding type. At about 8 feet from a wide plant bearing from fifty to a hundred flowers a combination plant close-up and scenic view is within the shortest focusing range of simple cameras. Where flowers are numerous and close together as they occur on beaver-tail cacti, close-ups within 3 or 4 feet

from the lens are very common with those who are skilled at making allowances for a deceiving view finder by slightly moving the camera one way or another to avoid cutting out desired details. A simple portrait-lens attachment for reasonably close-range focusing is their only accessory.

The Arizona barrel cacti, with large sizes of stems and flower crowns and their rigidity in a brisk wind, are very well suited for simple photography material. In southeastern Arizona there are stretches of desert where these cacti abound in colonies. And there are stretches where only a lone plant can be seen here and there or they seem to disappear altogether. But at a point beside the paved highway about 10 miles west of Benson, Arizona, and for a distance of about 15 miles in the direction of Tucson, Arizona, there is a plantation of Arizona barrel cacti that bloom faithfully in August, year after year. Red, yellow, and orange flower crowns atop the stems dot the desert for miles and miles. The flowers of the barrel cacti in this region are unusually large for the species *(Ferocactus Wislizenii)* and at the peak of their season, *which is the third week in August,* they form into circles and clusters that measure from 8 to 12 inches in diameter; the perfect arrangements for impressive semi-close-up photographs that can be made with simple-type cameras.

A great many people come to the desert region of the Southwest in spring to take pictures of cactus flowers and plants. Most of them do not fuss too much with the techniques of extreme close-up photography; yet they too can achieve excellent results, and by so doing fulfill their search for beauty.

$\mathcal{G}uibe$ TO THE FLOWERING CACTUS

CACTUS NAMES

Plant authorities — taxonomists and botanists — do not recognize common names used in literature to identify cactus plants. They are perfectly right, because in some species plants may be called by certain names in one locality, while the same species are better known by different names in another locality. For example: *Peniocereus Greggii* in some localities is known as sweet potato cactus; in others it is called chaparral cactus, night-blooming cereus, or Queen of the Night. Yet, these same names are applied to other species that are entirely unrelated. For the 1,600-odd species in the cactus family only 50 to 100 common names have been coined. In many instances one species may be burdened with a dozen or more common names.

In this book the editors have used all old established common names that are available. Since there are not enough to go around, names have been coined to offset the shortage. This is recognized by authorities to be a writer's privilege, since they do not concern themselves with common names. But for the layman common names are, admittedly, more digestible than the technical terms used in the language of botany.

There is, to a limited extent, some confusion in the botanical system of naming cacti, and various textbooks use names that often differ with other text books, but this is considered a difference of opinion rather than an error. For instance: *Ferocactus Wislizenii* is, by some writers, placed in the genus *Echinocactus*, a large genus that is split by some taxonomists into several small genera.

There are today three systems of technical cactus nomenclature. Any one is considered correct, or the mixing of the three systems, where a writer chooses.

In this book the editors have selected the technical names for cacti that are best known among the members of the cactus societies in America and Europe. For the reader who might wish to study cactus taxonomy, nomenclature, and the scientific biological aspects of this subject the books listed in the bibliography are recommended.

Common and botanical names, growing range, and best months for flowers. Page numbers in bold type indicate color photographs; page numbers in light type refer to text references, comprehensive pencil sketches, and black and white photographs.

PEYOTE BUTTON — *Lophophora Williamsii*

CATCLAW CACTUS — *Ferocactus uncinatus*

ARIZONA BAR▶
Ferocactus Wisliz

TORCH CEREUS — *Trichocereus Spachianus*

WARTY HEDGEHOG — *Echinocereus enneacanthus.*

LIVING ROCK — *Ariocarpus fissuratus.*

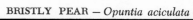

BRISTLY PEAR — *Opuntia aciculata*

PRICKLY ROSE — *Opuntia erinacea var. rhodantha.*

CHARTREUSE HEDGEHOG — *Echinomastus Johnsonii var. lutescens.*

INDIAN BASKET — *Echinomastus erectocentrus.*

TULIP PRICKLY PEAR — *Opuntia phaeacantha.*

ENGELMANN'S (STRAWBERRY) HEDGEHOG
Echinocereus Engelmannii

BIBLIOGRAPHY

BENSON, LYMAN. *The Cacti of Arizona.* University of New Mexico Press, Albuquerque, N.M., 1950.

BORG, J. *Cacti.* Macmillan & Co., Ltd., London, 1937.

BRITTON, N. L., and ROSE, J. N. *The Cactaceae.* 4 vols. Carnegie Institution, Washington, D.C., 1923. Reprinted by Abbey Garden Press, Pasadena, Calif., 1931.

HASELTON, S. E. *Epiphyllum Handbook.* Abbey Garden Press, Pasadena, Calif., 1946.

KEARNEY, T. H., and PEEBLES, R. H. *Arizona Flora.* University of California Press, Berkeley and Los Angeles, Calif., 1951.

MacDOUGAL, D. T. "Deserts and Their Plants," *Old and New Plant Lore,* part V; vol. II. *Smithsonian Scientific Series,* Washington, D. C., 1938.

MARSHALL, W. T. *Arizona's Cactuses.* Tempe, Arizona, Desert Botanical Garden, 1953.

MARSHALL, W. T., and BOCK, T. M. *Cactaceae.* Abbey Garden Press, Pasadena, Calif., 1941.

LOW GROWING PRICKLY PEAR CACTI

Ely

Tonopah

NEV.
UTAH

Panguitch

Cedar
City

Bishop

UTAH
ARIZ.

LARGEST BARREL CACTI IN THE U. S.

NEV.
CALIF.

Las
Vegas

Barstow

Kingman

Needles

Flagstaff

San Bernardino

Parker

Prescott

Riverside

Blythe

Seven
Springs

San Diego

CALIF.
ARIZ.

Phoenix

El Centro

CALIF.

LARGEST CACTI

Tijuana BAJA
CALIF. Mexicali

Yuma

IN THE U. S.

Coolidge

Ajo

Tucson

HOME
OF
THE
PRINGLE
CEREUS

SONORA

ARIZ.

MEXICO

Nogales

GREAT
NUMBER
OF
BOTH
LARGE
AND
SMALL
CACTI

San Felipe

Punta Peñasco

Cananea

GULF
OF
CALIFORNIA

CEREUS · LARGEST OF ALL CACTI

Altar

Santa Ana

Rosario

Puerto Libertad

MEXICO

Hermosillo

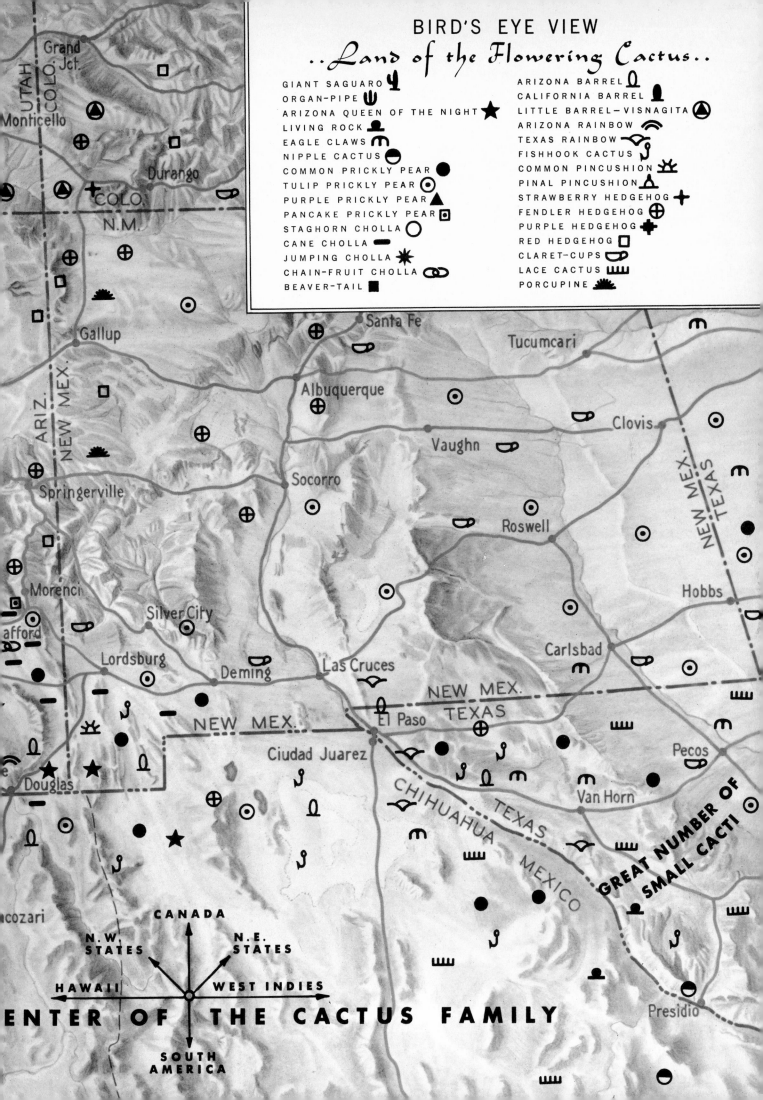

BIRD'S EYE VIEW

..Land of the Flowering Cactus..

GIANT SAGUARO
ORGAN-PIPE
ARIZONA QUEEN OF THE NIGHT
LIVING ROCK
EAGLE CLAWS
NIPPLE CACTUS
COMMON PRICKLY PEAR
TULIP PRICKLY PEAR
PURPLE PRICKLY PEAR
PANCAKE PRICKLY PEAR
STAGHORN CHOLLA
CANE CHOLLA
JUMPING CHOLLA
CHAIN-FRUIT CHOLLA
BEAVER-TAIL

ARIZONA BARREL
CALIFORNIA BARREL
LITTLE BARREL—VISNAGITA
ARIZONA RAINBOW
TEXAS RAINBOW
FISHHOOK CACTUS
COMMON PINCUSHION
PINAL PINCUSHION
STRAWBERRY HEDGEHOG
FENDLER HEDGEHOG
PURPLE HEDGEHOG
RED HEDGEHOG
CLARET-CUPS
LACE CACTUS
PORCUPINE

Grand Jct.
UTAH
COLO.
Monticello
Durango
COLO.
N.M.
Gallup
Santa Fe
Tucumcari
Albuquerque
Clovis
Vaughn
ARIZ.
NEW MEX.
Socorro
Roswell
Springerville
Hobbs
Morenci
Silver City
Carlsbad
afford
Lordsburg
Deming
Las Cruces
NEW MEX.
TEXAS
NEW MEX.
El Paso
TEXAS
Douglas
Ciudad Juarez
Pecos
CHIHUAHUA
Van Horn
NEW MEX.
TEXAS
cozari
CHIHUAHUA
MEXICO

GREAT NUMBER OF SMALL CACTI

CANADA
N.W. STATES
N.E. STATES
HAWAII
WEST INDIES
ENTER OF THE CACTUS FAMILY
SOUTH AMERICA
Presidio

OCOTILLO — *Fouquieria splendens*

YUCCA — *Yucca elata*

SPANISH BAYONET — *Yucca baccata*

CENTURY PLANT — *Agave Parryi*